P9-CPW-458

# I WANT TO BE LITTLE

By CHARLOTTE ZOLOTOW • Pictures by TONY DE LUNA

Abelard-Schuman

London NewYork Toronto

 Library of Congress Catalogue Card Number: AC 66-10760
First published in Great Britain in 1967. Printed in the United States of America

Once there was a little girl.
Everyone asked her, "What do you want to be when you grow up?"
"I want to stay little," she said.

"Why?" asked her father, surprised.
"Because," said the little girl.
"Because why?" asked her father.

“Well,” said the little girl, “I want
to be little so I can skip.
Grownups don’t skip.

I want to be little so I can jump rope.
Grownups don't jump rope.

I want to be little to go to birthday parties
with candles and cake and balloons.
Grownups don't have that kind of birthday party.

I want to be little to fit under the piano.
Grownups never do.

I want to be little to go barefoot.
Grownups don't.

I want to be little to jump in leaves in the fall.
Grownups don't.

I want to be little so that I can eat snow.
Grownups don't.

I like to be little so I can play with dolls.
Grownups don't play with dolls.

I like to be little so I can be
tucked in bed at night.
Grownups don't get tucked in bed at night.

I like to be little to play in the park.
Grownups don't play in the park.

I like to be little to turn
summersaults when I'm glad.
Grownups don't turn summersaults.

I like to be little to cry when I'm sad.
Grownups don't.

I like to be little so that I can
sit on people's laps.
Grownups don't sit on people's laps.

I like to be little because I can
be kissed by everyone who likes me.
Grownups can't be kissed by everyone who likes them.

I can grow up to be a ballet dancer
or a writer

or a nurse
and a mother.

But meanwhile
I want to be little."

And she summersaulted out of the room.